Sergeant O'Keefe

and His Mule, Balaam

BY HAROLD W. FELTON

Illustrated by Leonard Everett Fisher

DODD, MEAD & COMPANY, NEW YORK

To Frances and Elmer

A NOTE FROM THE AUTHOR

ONCE UPON A TIME there was a man who was in charge of a weather station of the United States Army Signal Corps on the top of Pikes Peak. The man was a sergeant, but he was also one of those persons whom nature had endowed with the ability to spin a tall yarn in such a way that it was passed on. It is an art given to but few.

The man's name was John T. O'Keefe, or perhaps it was John T. O'Keeffe. One can't be sure exactly how a tall-tale teller's name is spelled. His mule, though, was named Balaam. Sergeant O'Keefe spoke with a melodious Irish brogue, but on one occasion found cause to announce that he was a native of Italy. A tall-tale teller must not be contradicted, a circumstance not known to one Cherokee Charley, a notorious desperado. An argument ensued and both men found themselves in jail. Funds not being readily available, the sergeant pawned his mule in order to bail 'em. Of course, the mule became known as Balaam.

Most readers will be able to glean the principal biographical details concerning Sergeant O'Keefe from the text. But tall tales being what they are, it may satisfy some curiosity and lingering

5

doubt if it is made clear that I have pursued the evidence in the early newspaper stories and have made inquiries elsewhere.

The name is spelled O'Keefe in most of the available printed material. The Naval Academy recognizes this as the spelling. The sergeant's Army record, however, is under the name of O'Keeffe. The Signal Corps Historical Division says his name was spelled O'Keefe in the record of his first enlistment, and O'Keeffe in the record of his second enlistment and other records. His weather reports and related correspondence reveal that he signed his name O'Keeffe, at least in the last few years of his Army service.

His obituary, which appeared in the Denver *Rocky Mountain News* of February 3, 1895, reveals that he died on February 2 of that year and that he was thirty-nine years old. That would make the date of his birth 1856. On the other hand, Army records disclose that he re-enlisted on May 1, 1879, and on that date was aged 25 and 4/12, and that he had gray eyes and black hair. Thus, his birth would have been in 1854. Both records agree, however, as does that of the Naval Academy, that he was born in New York City. Substantial numbers of O'Keefes and O'Keeffes were born in these years in New York City, but I find no record that can fairly be said to be that of our hero's birth in that town.

The obituary also reveals that O'Keefe entered the Naval Academy at Annapolis in 1872, that "for two years he studied like a Trojan and was at the head of his class at the termination of each year," and that he was expelled for hazing. The Naval Academy records agree, at least in part. He entered in 1872 but, sadly and prosaically, "he was found deficient in Mathematics and in French and was dropped from the rolls of the Naval Academy on 13 June 1873."

Some of the differences in the biographical details may be due to error in transmission, in hearing and reporting. Some may be due to the tall-tale telling fancy which seems at times to be irresistible. And herein lies at least part of the reason why it seems unnecessary to me to tell a story exactly as the last person told it. A dull, static, unromantic coldness is almost bound to result. Therefore, I have truthened the stories up a little when it seemed to me to be desirable. General Hiram Chittenden, in his book *The Yellowstone National Park*, has commented on changes in tall tales, saying that it is a fortunate thing that these stories grow and develop with time, gravitating always from the real to the ideal. Put another way—in General Chittenden's terms—I have only gravitated the tales a bit.

Everyone can enjoy tall tales, and almost everyone does. The humor of exaggeration has a wide and common base. One of the gentlemen who by reason of training, occupation and inclination is entitled to have an opinion about Sergeant O'Keefe and his story-telling ability is Duncan Emrich. In his book, *It's an Old Wild West Custom*, Mr. Emrich says:

"The loneliness of certain occupations forced men to become humorists to retain their sanity, and one such was Sergeant John T. O'Keefe, who spent three years in the 1870's on Pikes Peak recording wind velocities, rain and snowfalls, temperatures, and other phenomena for the United States Signal Corps."

Levette J. Davidson and Forrester Blake, editors of *Rocky Mountain Tales*, include in their book some of the stories of Sergeant O'Keefe and his mule which were printed in the *Colorado Springs Gazette*, the *Rocky Mountain News*, and the "Annual Report of the Chief Signal-Officer, for 1875," *Report of the Secretary of War to the Forty-Fourth Congress, 1876*. They point to the collaborative reports of O'Keefe and Balaam as combining "an Irishman's indestructible level-headedness with an American's raucous enthusiasms for the incomprehensible." They, like Mr. Emrich, are well qualified to have opinions of tall tales and tall-tale tellers. The newspaper stories were widely reprinted at the time. The sergeant's talents were recognized during his lifetime, good fortune all too seldom given the true artist.

At the time of his departure from the Pikes Peak Signal Office in 1881 Sergeant O'Keefe was renowned as the Prevaricator of Pikes Peak. A banquet was given in his honor which was reported in both the *Rocky Mountain News* and the *Colorado Springs Gazette* on December 21 and 22, 1881, respectively.

It was quite an affair, at the opera house. Guests sat down to four generously provided tables in the body of the house. The parquet circle, the balcony and the gallery were crowded with spectators, indication of the popularity of the Sergeant and the esteem in which he was held. These spectators, it is reported, testfied to their enjoyment of the evening by frequent bursts of applause.

The presiding officer was Lieutenant H. P. Scott, city editor of the local newspaper. The president, raising his glass of Iron Ute water, proposed the following toast: "O'Keefe, one of the greatest prevaricators, equalled by few, excelled by none. True to his record, may his life be a romance and in his final resting place may he lie easy." After which, Lieutenant Scott expressed a deep appreciation in words certainly equal to the occasion: "The rosy realms of romance are as real to O'Keefe as the stern and sterile steppes of truth are to many. The golden glow which gilds the granite summit of the Peak is but the type of that glamour which surrounds it through the mendacious genius of O'Keefe. This aureole envelopes the mountain and some of O'Keefe's legends—are more stupendous than the Peak itself."

Many notables were present at the banquet, speeches were made, and Alderman Ainsworth Brown read an original poem "in tones trembling with emotion" which began:

> Assist me now divine poetic fire,
> Come to my aid and help me strike the lyre.

Little wonder the reporter concluded with the observation that the banquet was "one of the most interesting events of the year in Colorado Springs."

Balaam, that most glorious of all mules, received at least some of the honor due her, and during her lifetime, too, in the form of a longish poem in which the poet got the poor mule's sex mixed up.

> He traced a long, unbroken line
> Of proud relations asinine.

In spite of this distressing circumstance, not surprising in tall-tale circles, it was a noble tribute to a living mule. After relating some of Balaam's adventures in rhyme, the poet, Mr. Charles Craig, concludes:

> With heels and tail aloft in air,
> Old Balaam scampers o'er the plain,
> While lifts the poets conscious hair
> And wildly throbs his swelling brain,
> As thoughts of what e'en mules may dare
> In this great country of light air!

Thus, here is a view that the thin air of Pikes Peak may have induced the airy flights of the mule and, one may suppose, of the Sergeant, too.

The newspaper stories disclose that Mr. O'Keefe, after he left the Signal Corps, worked for the Colorado Telegraph Co. of Denver, later as a railway mail agent, and that he was a member of the Denver Fire Department at the time of his death. The editors of *Rocky Mountain Tales* reveal that his grave has long since disappeared.

Grave stones and markers fail. His name may be spelled in more than one way. There may be disagreement as to the date of birth. Other ordinary factual details may be in a state of confusion. But there was a spark within the man that kindled happy mendacities and brought the words to his tongue's tip to express them. They give us a picture of a soldier and an Army mule, and, more important, continued smiles and perhaps a chuckle or two.

—HAROLD W. FELTON

New York City
April, 1962

CONTENTS

Strange Doings
on Pikes Peak

"H ERE COMES Sergeant O'Keefe," said Judge Eliphalet Price.

"Where?" asked Mr. Sweeney as he stepped out of the telegraph office.

For answer, the Judge pointed down the dusty street. "And he has Balaam with him."

It was in truth Sergeant John Timothy O'Keefe. He was riding Balaam, the ancient dapple-gray Army mule, the Sergeant's constant companion, friend and participant in the strange and wonderful adventures that occurred in the thin air on the slopes and summit of Pikes Peak.

And they in turn were followed by Hobbs who was riding the bay mule, Kit. The mules kicked up little puffs of dust at each step as they walked down the main street of Colorado Springs. At length they turned in to the hitching rail that ran along next to the plank sidewalk which stretched its way from building to building.

"Howdy, Sergeant," said Judge Price.

"Top o' the mornin' to ye, Judge," replied the tall soldier as he dismounted and curled his mule's reins around the hitching rail and stepped up to the wooden sidewalk.

O'Keefe's face was deep-tanned by wind and weather. He carried himself well as a soldier does, especially a soldier who, nine years before, had spent a year as cadet midshipman at the United States Naval Academy. It was an unfortunate deficiency in mathematics and in French which had turned him to a career as a noncommissioned officer in the United States Army Signal Corps, and had lost him a commission in the Navy.

It was 1881. Sergeant O'Keefe, tall, trim and muscular, was twenty-five years old. He had jet black hair and a thin but nevertheless substantial mustache. His gray eyes twinkled promise of humorous story or adventure. His tongue was quick and delivered words in a flowing stream, words that sparkled with just a bit of Irish brogue.

If difficulty with French and mathematics had prevented John Timothy O'Keefe from becoming a Naval officer, the Army Signal Corps was the winner. He was a good soldier. He had been assigned to the Signal Corps weather station atop Pikes Peak, and there he performed his duties. Perhaps his blouse was not always as neat as required by regulations, but O'Keefe was on hand when there was a job to do. The dark stain on his sleeve would no doubt bring a scowl from an officer, but it was there because a grateful mule had given him a friendly nudge with a wet muzzle.

O'Keefe was a good man with Army mules. They worked for him. They liked him, and he liked them. Like a mule,

O'Keefe could be stubborn. He was strong, too. He was loyal and enduring at hard work, but, like a mule, he did not use all his strength unless it was necessary.

Strangely, John Timothy O'Keefe was graced with unusually large ears, and he could make them move. As a boy he had achieved considerable fame because he was able to wiggle his ears. Now that he was a man he carried his large ears without self-consciousness. Foolish soldiers who had tried to compare his ears to those of a mule received only a grin instead of an angry reply. To tell the truth, John O'Keefe was proud of his outsize, movable ears.

Balaam, the durable, dapple-gray Army mule was also assigned to the Pikes Peak weather station. She was older than the young sergeant, and she stood fourteen hands high. Her long, solemn, wise and sadly beautiful face was punctuated by two dark, lustrous eyes, and crowned by two of the longest, most agile and expressive ears that ever graced a mule's head. In the fashion of an Army mule, her mane was roached and the upper part of her tail was clipped smooth while the brush of it hung straight and clean, trimmed to the proper Army length.

The wisdom of years shone in Balaam's eyes and her dapple-gray hide was marked with the scars of old saddle sores and harness burns. Army records held the secret of Balaam's long and honorable military career. No one in Colorado Springs knew of all the caissons or Army supply wagons she had pulled. Nor did they know the campaigns she had served in or the battles she had seen. But everyone knew that Balaam was the first Army mule ever to reach the summit of Pikes Peak, and that was enough honor for any creature. Everyone knew, too, that Balaam had served at the weather station of the Army Signal Corps continuously since that first day when she stood triumphantly on the Peak and, overlooking the waves of foothills and countless miles of prairies to the east, had brayed her song loud and clear.

Other Rocky Mountain canaries since then had sung their songs on the great Peak, but none could equal Balaam, the greatest Rocky Mountain canary of them all.

Balaam was a sturdy Army mule, an enduring, faithful, hard-working creature. It was her everyday task to conquer the dangerous trails etched in the dizzy heights of the majestic peak, and she did it with aplomb. In a way, Pikes Peak stands as a monument to Balaam. Captain Zebulon Montgomery Pike may have discovered the mountain on Thanksgiving Day, November 27, 1806, but he did not climb it. On the other hand, Balaam climbed it constantly. History is what it is, and it is probably too late now to call it Balaam's Peak, but it does seem that somewhere in its vicinity there ought to be at least a little hill that could be used as a memorial to Balaam, even if it were called Balaam's Hump, or possibly Balaam's Bump.

"Tell me," said Sergeant O'Keefe suddenly. "Have ye seen a bit of a change in the Peak?"

Mr. Sweeney and Judge Price cupped their hands above their eyes and gazed up at the heavy line of Pikes Peak, the stone horizon that loomed above them in the distance.

"I have noticed no change," said Judge Price.

"Me neither," said Mr. Sweeney.

Mr. Sweeney was a soldier who enjoyed his meals, and showed it. His Army blouse, large as it was, was not big enough for Mr. Sweeney, especially after meals. It was usually straining at the buttons, cigar ashes decorated its broad expanse, and it was often dotted with spots and splashes of spilled food.

Mr. Sweeney was also in the service of the U. S. Army Signal Corps, as was Mr. Hobbs. He did not boast the rank of sergeant, and was not likely to. But as assistant to Sergeant O'Keefe at the weather station, he was a good man. So was Hobbs. Even a man such as the Sergeant could not operate a weather station all alone. He had to have some help. Yes, Hobbs was a good man, too. Not as big as Mr. Sweeney, and not as fat. But he was just as good a soldier, and just as good, too, at working the weather station instruments. One of the Signal Corps relief men was at the station at the moment. There would be no interruption in the service while the Sergeant was in Colorado Springs with both Hobbs and Sweeney.

Sergeant O'Keefe and his companions made their way over to the shade of the tall cottonwood trees that were in a vacant lot between the telegraph office and the post office. The newspaper building was nearby, along with the few stores of growing Colorado Springs. Business was transacted on the sturdy plank benches that stretched from tree to tree, but for the most part it was a place to meet and talk and laugh.

When Sergeant John Timothy O'Keefe arrived there was little inclination to continue whatever idle conversation was in progress. Even business deals were put aside for the moment. The tall, jovial Irishman loved to talk, and when he came down from the weather station atop the Peak

there was usually something to talk about.

He addressed the group now.

"Tell me, then, what would you think if you was to come outdoors some mornin' and look up there to the Peak and see it bald and bare as a dark brown egg? What would ye think then?" the Sergeant demanded.

"Well, this time of the year, I'd think there was something powerful wrong," Judge Price replied.

Judge Eliphalet Price was much taller than Mr. Sweeney, and not as fat. As a matter of fact, Judge Eliphalet Price was not fat at all. He was thin. Tall and thin. Skinny, the soldiers said. Sergeant O'Keefe always said that the Judge was so thin he had to stand sideways to make a shadow. If he did not stand sideways, he had to stand in the same place twice before a bright sun could make a shadow with the extraordinarily lean Judge Price. He had been a judge in the mountain gold camps. He had made some money there in business ventures. Since then he had been a newspaper reporter and correspondent for eastern newspapers. The Judge was always carefully groomed, and wore his tall hat and neat frock coat with considerable grace.

"You would be wonderin' after the safety of the men and the beasts up there on the Peak, would ye not?" Sergeant O'Keefe continued.

"I suppose so. Yes," said Judge Price.

"Then what I did was right," the young soldier said with a sigh of relief. It was a satisfied sigh that let his straight white teeth flash diamonds below his dark mustache.

"What did you do?" the Judge asked.

The Sergeant seemed not to hear. "Yes, sir. Balaam

started singin' early in the mornin'. Long before the sun poked his head up over the never-endin' prairie to the east. Never before had I heard her, or any other Rocky Mountain canary, sing like that."

" 'Something is wrong, turrible, turrible wrong,' I said to meself. Out of the door I go and, begorra, there before me eyes I saw a sight that never did I see before and, praise be, I hope I never will see again."

"What? What did you see?" asked the Judge.

"No snow," said the Sergeant.

"No snow?"

"Yes. No snow!" The Sergeant's words were measured and deliberate, and they breathed from his lips, making the hairs on his upper lip tremble.

He was ready with more words. "Not a flake of snow. No hide nor hair of snow. Not a smidgin of snow," he said.

"What had happened?"

"That's what I am tellin' ye. The volcano came to life. That's what happened."

"Volcano?" asked Mr. Sweeney with a puzzled voice.

"There is no volcano on Pikes Peak," Judge Price said with conviction.

"Sure and bejeepers, that is what everyone thinks," the Sergeant agreed. "But the Peak is of volcanic origin, though praise be to heaven there has been no active volcano there since the memory of man runneth not to the contrary. In me bones I have felt that someday it would come to life, and that is just what it did, it did indeed."

"No!" said Mr. Sweeney. He had come down to Colorado Springs the day before to see to messages at the telegraph

office. The happenings on the Peak in his absence were
almost too much to believe.

"Yes," said the Sergeant.

"Well, what d'ye know!" said Mr. Sweeney.

"But the snow? What happened to the snow?" asked
Eliphalet Price.

"Ah, yes. The snow. Sure, and the heat from the hot
heart of the volcano melted the snow and not a drift, not
even a small flake of the white stuff, remained. There was
no snow at all, at all.

"Well, now, thinks I, if the good people down in Colorado Springs wake up this fine mornin' and see no snow on
the summit, they will have a fit for themselves, and me
friends will be worried for me safety. More than that, tour-
ists will never come to see a big mountain with no snow on
it. 'Twould be a turrible thing, indeed it would.

"Balaam, she was singin' away like the poor heart inside
her would break. Poor creature that she is, she had no way
of knowin' what had happened, nor why. I got her quieted
down by whisperin' some sweet nothin's in her ear. Then,
said I to meself, I have to do something. Colorado Springs
will never be the same. It will be just another town sittin'
at the foot of a mountain. Sweeney had left the day before.
Hobbs and Kit were off repairing a broken telegraph line.
It was up to me. I had to do something meself."

"But there is snow up there now," said Judge Price.

"Good," said O'Keefe.

"What do you mean, 'good,'?" one of the other men asked.

"Look at the Peak, and ye see snow. Leastways, you think
it is snow. Indeed I am pleased, I am indeed," said the

Sergeant. "Now I know that all of me trouble was worth-while."

"What trouble?"

"You look up there at it, seventeen miles as the mule walks and I don't know how far as the crow flies, for no crow that I know of has ever flown it. And you see snow. Ah, I am that glad. Indeed I am."

"But what was worthwhile?" the Judge demanded.

"Yes. What?" Mr. Sweeney echoed.

"Sure, I told you the volcano had melted all of the snow on the Peak. Such a thing should never be, as I well know. Such a mountain as that, a giant mountain of a mountain, without no snow on her rock bald noggin!"

The Sergeant warmed to his tale. "I got meself busy. The water from the melted snow flooded the gullies. I built me-self a dam so as to hold back the water. Then I directed the dammed up water past the chalk cliff on the upper western slope. I worked hard, I can tell you. It was a good thing the view from down here in Colorado Springs was blocked off by some clouds that hung low below the Peak this mornin'. That was the reason you didn't notice how bald and bereft of snow she was. Sure and bejeepers, but up there on the top I was workin', I can tell you."

"But doin' what?" repeated Mr. Sweeney.

"I mixed the water with the chalk from the white chalk cliffs, and I painted the summit where the snow was not, and where the snow should be.

"Balaam, she helped me. She did indeed. I'm sure I don't know what I would have done without that darlin' mule. She used that beautiful brush of a tail on the south end of herself. Sure, and she worked like a trooper right along with me. She was splashin' that whitewash and I was splashin' that whitewash, and we whitewashed the top of Pikes Peak!''

"No!" exclaimed Mr. Sweeney.

"Yes, sir!" the Sergeant replied. "Indeed we did. We did indeed. By the time Hobbs came back, we had the job done. It was a big job, but once I start a job I don't quit easy. You can look up there right this blessed minute and see for yourself that it is as white as wintertime at the north pole.''

"So it is," said Eliphalet Price.

"And," continued Sergeant John Timothy O'Keefe, "now, begorra, volcano or no volcano, Pikes Peak will have a noble crown that looks like snow, whether snow is up there or not.''

"Well, what do ye know?" said Mr. Sweeney.

A Real
Valuable Mule

S ERGEANT John Timothy O'Keefe was sitting on a rock
at the side of the Army Signal Corps weather station. Hobbs
and Sweeney sat close by. The wind was clear and cool, but
it could not reach around the protecting corners of the stone
building. The sun shone down warmly on the three men as
they basked in its gentle rays there on top of the world.

It was midsummer, but on the Peak, rock-bare and snow-
splashed, the feel of spring was in the air. It was a magic day
in the warm, sheltered area. It was the kind of day that in
another part of the world would call for marbles, hopscotch,
rope skipping and all the other childhood delights of the
first warm days after a long winter.

But to three soldiers of the Army Signal Corps, the day
demanded no such games. However much the three guard-
ians of the weather station may have thought of such bygone
pleasures, they said nothing about them. But they talked.
Talk was cheap and, besides, there was nothing else to do

at the moment. They, with the mules, gloried in the warm rays of the sun.

The solid, compact bodies of the mules were motionless except for the faint breath of movement showing in their tails and in soft flicks of shoulder or flank, which revealed that they were ready and able to protect themselves from the first insect that dared to approach their sleek sides.

Long mule ears slanted at ease. Lazy lids, guarded by long lashes, fell as curtains, leaving slim slits before their drowsy eyes. They looked asleep, but they were Army mules, and Army mules never sleep. They drowse, and that is what Balaam and Kit were doing.

If Kit was motionless, Balaam seemed carved in dapple-gray stone. She knew how to rest. The slant of her ears gave great nobility to a noble mule's head. Although the slope of Kit's long ears produced undoubted aesthetic angles, Balaam's longer, beautifully whiskered aural appendages created artistic lines that went far beyond mere beauty. They spoke of aplomb, assurance, character.

"You know," said Sergeant O'Keefe, "as I see it, Balaam is one of the most valuable creatures in the world."

Hobbs and Sweeney both nodded. Their first thoughts took their memories to the many times Balaam had proven that she was the peer of all Army mules. There was no doubt about it. Balaam was a valuable mule. She was a dapple-gray treasure.

But one of the most valuable creatures in the world? Hobbs's sun-soothed mind worked slowly up and down the list of valuable animals as he stretched his short legs out before him.

" 'Course," he said, "any good mule is valuable." Balaam certainly was a good mule. Oh, well, he might let it all drop right there. Hobbs was not a soldier who liked to think. The warm sun was taking over. Why trouble to think further?

"The best," O'Keefe said.

"Well, yes. The best, then," Hobbs agreed. "I suppose so." It would be easier to agree than to think more about it.

"Funny thing about mules it is," said O'Keefe. "Sure, and one parent is an ass and one is a horse. They are hybrids, and can never be parents themselves. But the sire must be the ass, a jack, that is. And the dam must be the horse, the mare, that is."

"I don't think I ever heard that before, Johnny," said Hobbs. "I was raised up in a city, and I never had much to do with mules and such like before I joined the Army."

"If it is the other way around," the Sergeant continued, "that is, if the sire is the horse, a stallion, you know, and if he is mated with a jenny, that is, a female ass, the result is not the same. Not the same at all, at all. In such a case, the offspring is called a hinney. And while a hinney looks somewhat like a mule, it has nowhere near all the fine qualities.

"Sure, and it is the truth, a mule is a favorite creature of both God and man. And although they say a mule has no pride of ancestry and no hope of posterity, the fine blood of great horses and of great donkeys meet in the beautiful creature known as a mule.

"Mules have the best characteristics of their parents," O'Keefe went on. "Of the both of them. Asses are enduring, patient and strong. Horses are fast and intelligent and strong. Mules are all of these things, and more. They are smarter, begorra, than either of their parents. They live longer. They are more resistant to disease and climate. They are surer-footed and have a better sense of balance, that they do."

Sergeant O'Keefe was speaking from long experience with mules. He knew they were truly noble creatures and he could be eloquent about them. He could also be eloquent with them. He had the vocabulary and the voice.

"Golly, I didn't know all of that, Johnny," said Hobbs.

"Out on the prairies they say a man without a horse ain't a man," said O'Keefe.

"He'd be a man if he had a mule," put in Sweeney.

"Yes, he would that. But cowboys ain't much used to mules," the Sergeant said. "A man workin' in the mountains ain't a man if he hasn't got a mule. And many a cowboy has forked a mule to good advantage. The mountain men in the early days almost always used mules. So did those traders on the Santa Fe trail."

" 'Course," said Sweeney as he shifted on his rock, "bein' valuable and bein' a good mule and all of that is one thing. Bein' one of the most valuable creatures in the whole world is another thing." Sweeney made his announcement sagely.

"Sweeney's right, Johnny," Hobbs agreed. "How do you figure Balaam's as valuable as all that?"

"A mule is a useful and honorable citizen," said Sweeney. "A mule is a soldier, and a good one, as everybody from a private to a general knows. You can't hardly soldier in the mountains at all without mules."

"Or on the plains, either," Hobbs added.

"Or on the plains, either," Sweeney agreed. "But—"

"I can see ye don't agree with me, so I'll tell you what that mule is worth," O'Keefe announced. "Balaam was the first mule ever to breathe the thin and rare air here at the top of Pikes Peak at an altitude of something over 14,000 feet above the level of the sea."

"I don't see that adds anything towards makin' her valuable," said Hobbs.

"Sure, and that just goes to show that your imagination is not everything it might be," the Sergeant replied. "Mr. Phineas Taylor Barnum could use that mule in his circus just on that ground alone. I shouldn't wonder at all, at all, but that lots of people would pay good money just to see such a famous animal."

"Well, yes," Hobbs admitted. Why hadn't he thought of that?

John Timothy O'Keefe went on. "Balaam, bless every bone in that darlin' mule, has traveled up and down Pikes Peak to Colorado Springs a total of 3,849 times."

"Round trips, or one way?" asked Sweeney.

"One way, of course. Sure, that is one thing I should think you might know. If it had been round trips, it would have to be so-and-so many times and a half. If not, she'd be down in Colorado Springs, and you can see with your own eyes that the darlin' handsome creature is standin' here before you as big as life. Yes, indeed, 3,849 times." He paused to let the figure be impressive.

"That's seventeen miles each way. Multiply that by 3,849 and you have—now let me see." He scratched figures in a dusty layer of fine sand that had blown on the sheltered side

of the station. Sweeney and Hobbs leaned toward him, Sweeney to check on the figures and Hobbs to watch more closely and observe this interesting process which was far beyond any skill he had with numbers.

"There. That makes at total of 65,433 miles, bejeepers. Yes, sir, it does indeed. The earth is almost 25,000 miles around, at the equator. So, while Balaam has been stationed here at Pikes Peak she has gone a distance of more than twice around the world!"

"No!" said Hobbs as his eyes bugged out.

"More than two-and-a-half times around the world. That's a lot of walkin', begorra."

Sweeney's jaw dropped. "Well, what do ye know?" he breathed.

"And mountain travel, every single step of the weary way. Steep, hard mountain trails."

"And she never fell down once," Hobbs added. "Never stumbled."

"In all that time," O'Keefe continued, "I figure that darlin' mule has worn out 560 sets of shoes, equal in weight to about a ton of iron. Sure, and you must figure that in, too, when you figure her value. It takes a blacksmith about two hours to shoe a mule. That would be 1,120 hours of a blacksmith's time. Figure ten hours a day. Let's see, that would be 112 days, just for the blacksmith. Figure six workin' days a week. That would be, hmmm, let's see. That would be 18 and two-thirds weeks of a blacksmith's time it has taken for nothin' more than to keep her darlin' feet in shoes, bejeepers."

"What do ye know?" was all that Sweeney was able to say

in the presence of such learning.

" 'Course, that doesn't take into account what walkin' she has done besides, like goin' to follow the telegraph wires, goin' for wood and water, and just plain moseyin' around like a mule does sometimes."

"Well, what do ye know?" Sweeney was truly amazed.

"Then," continued O'Keefe, "she eats a peck of oats a day. Just in the last seven years she has eaten 2,555 pecks of oats, or—" He scratched in the sand again. "Or 638 and three-quarters bushels. She eats a bale of hay a week. That would make, let's see. That would make 364 bales of hay, and I haven't even figured the cost of blankets, saddles, bridles, halters and harness and the likes of that."

"Well, what do ye know?" came from Sweeney once again.

O'Keefe ran on. "Then you've got to remember all of that is only for the seven years Balaam has been on Pikes Peak. She must be 32 years old, give or take a bit. She must of started to work by the time she was four, or three years old maybe. So sure, and you must multiply everything by four again, or even five maybe. And I've got no way of knowin' how many artillery caissons she has worn out or doubletrees likewise. Or how many neck yokes, singletrees, kingpins, wagon tongues and the like. There is more history in that mule than is in a dozen of the highest officers in the whole Signal Corps."

Sergeant John Timothy O'Keefe might have gone on and on, for Balaam was his favorite subject. But the sun was sinking below the jagged western horizon, and its warmth was going fast. It was getting on near supper time, too.

"I always knew Balaam was valuable because of what she

knows and does," Hobbs said. "But I never thought to figure it out before." He sighed deeply. "Havin' an education sure is a wonderful thing, Johnny."

"Well, what do ye know?" said Sweeney.

"A real valuable mule, that she is," O'Keefe breathed softly.

One Mule-Powered
Flying Machine

A T THE WEATHER station on top of the mountain the soldiers of the Army Signal Corps kept the instruments in order, read them at proper hours and telegraphed the information to Colorado Springs where it was relayed to other stations and used in the preparation of weather forecasts. Temperature, wind direction and speed, barometric pressure, precipitation and the physical appearance of the immense area below and around the great height were of greatest importance. Prompt reports were necessary. Accuracy was imperative.

The activities not merely of the Army, but of farmers, ranchers and business men were based on the weather studies and the conclusions of the Signal Corps.

From their vantage point in the sky atop Pikes Peak, at the foot of heaven, Signal Corps observers could see the weather for great distances in every direction.

Pikes Peak towered above the lesser mountains to the

35

south and north and west. There, half a century before, the mountain men had broken the first trails of the white men. Beaver trappers, exploring countless unknown canyons, deserts and mountain ranges, had done their work for miners, ranchers and business men who were to follow.

From Pikes Peak a man could look above the heads of jagged mountains in three directions to distant mountain ranges. The Peak loomed above the foothills and overlooked the level plains to the east. There the distances visible were so great and the spaces so vast that it took two men, both looking at the same time, to see as far as the horizon. A single man, with merely two eyes, could not see such a great distance.

The storms, or the lack of storms, in the huge expanse below the towering mountain made important weather news. A broken telegraph wire was a catastrophe. Repairs must be made at once. The work of John Timothy O'Keefe and his fellow soldiers of the Signal Corps was very important. Sergeant O'Keefe knew it. He saw that repairs were made promptly and reports sent on time.

But there was no reason to overdo things. O'Keefe was a soldier and a soldier should mind his manners. Supplies had to be obtained in Colorado Springs at the foot of the Peak. The telegraph office was there. Trips into the town were necessary, and when in town, of course it would be impolite not to pause and pass the time of day with his friends. John Timothy O'Keefe had stopped for a chat with Judge Price.

"Has the volcano been quiet lately?" asked Eliphalet Price.

The Sergeant seemed not to hear the question, although

he shifted his gaze from the distant bulk of the Peak to the Judge.

"I wouldn't of mentioned it, Judge, if you hadn't asked me," O'Keefe said finally. "A strange thing happened to me less than three weeks past. So strange it was that I wouldn't tell it without your question.

"Begorra, it had been a weird night, black and mysterious it was. Black as the inside of a coal miner's glove, with doleful sounds seemin' to rise out of the bowels of the earth.

"When I stepped out of the door, the mornin' was gray. Never had I seen the likes of it before. The sun seemed to struggle to raise itself above the level line at the end of the plains in the east, as if, begorra, it was fearful of risin' at all, at all. It had a dull, forbiddin', occult look, and while the sky was cloudless, it seemed covered with a sick, dull red screen and gave a cold, haze-burdened kind of light.

"Sure, it was like no day I have ever seen before. I went to the barn to bid me darlin' mule the top o' the mornin' and give herself her feed.

"When I forked her hay into the manger, I saw that her ears were slanted away at distressingly somber angles. She munched her oats like a small boy who had eaten too much candy the night before. She was without appetite, and she worked at her hay without the joy of eatin' that most usually fills her beautiful heart.

"I made me own breakfast but, sure, I didn't feel like eatin' neither. An Army mule and a Signal Corps sergeant not feelin' hungry! Can you imagine the likes of that? Sure, it was a rare day indeed. Indeed it was.

"The telegraph was not workin'. The wire was busted,

and it must be repaired. Hobbs and Sweeney were away on essential duties. I must get on with it meself. Faithful to me duty at the end of such a dire night and the beginning of such a somber day, I saddled me loyal beast of burden. In all of me life I had never seen such a day before, begorra. 'No good can come from this day,' I said.

"For answer, Balaam stretched her neck and sang a sad song. The song of the Rocky Mountain canary that usually filled me heart with its good spirit came to me on this cheerless day as a lachrymose lament. Its echo struck me ears with melancholy heaviness.

"Sure, on this day of no clouds and as yet no dawn, me and me darlin' mule made our way down the narrow, treacherous trail in the service of the United States Army Signal Corps. The telegraph wire was broken. Duty called, and me and me mule answered our sworn duty.

"As Balaam picked her way along the path, the strange mutterin's of the earth increased. Rocks moved from their places far above us on the sheer wall at our side. They slipped away and then fell, striking the face of the cliff with glancin' blows, scatterin' jagged pieces of stone on the trail and bouncin' off into the silence of the void below.

"In the midst of this turmoil, with rocks bouncin' all around us, me and me faithful companion made our way down the dangerous trail.

"Faith, and it was not long before we come to a place where the face of the sheer wall above us fell back and the trail edged away from the precipice on the other side. That mysterious noise we had been hearin' grew louder now. The world became depressin' indeed. The dull redness became duller. A small sound of thunder drew me eyes up the slope of the mountain. I saw a movement up there.

" 'Whoa,' says I. 'What in the name of heaven is that?'

"Balaam turned her head. Her long beautiful ears pointed toward this new sound.

" 'Looks like it is comin' this way, bejeepers,' I said as I tried to pierce the dullness of the air with me keen eyes.

"Although it was like lookin' through dirty pink lemonade, I saw what seemed to be a stream. Sure, and it moved like water. Steadily it advanced. It grew closer, a fog of smoke risin' above it. Then it seemed to move faster. And faster still. It dropped sharply and picked up speed. It seemed to be a narrow, most rapidly movin' stream now, dull red. A glow of red fog hovered about it and sped along with the speed of it.

"It spread apart and one fork of it headed out in front of me and me mule. The other fork darted, on purpose it seemed to me, in the other direction. It would go behind us.

" 'Whatever it is, it is goin' to miss us,' I remarked.

"It was close in front of us now, and I looked down. Then the truth, begorra, the distressin' truth dawned on me.

"It was lava! Molten, steamin' lava. And we were caught between the two searin' hot fingers of it.

" 'We've got to jump it,' I said, desperate-like.

" 'No, can't do it. It's too wide,' I answered meself.

"But Balaam, intelligent mule that she is, seemed to know what was necessary. She felt me own lack of determination. She stretched her neck out sharp-like, and pulled the reins through me hands. The leather burned me fingers.

"In this split moment, the indecision I had was overcome

by Balaam's determination. Movin' as light as a butterfly, she danced back a few steps until her heels were almost singed by the flamin' stream behind us. Quick as the flick of her tail, she took a short run and before I could stop her, she jumped. That she did. It must of been a record for a short runnin' jump for mules. Sure, and if a person had told me about it, I swear I would have been hard pressed to believe it. But I saw it meself. Together we soared over that burnin' stream of lava that faced us.

"No more than in the nick of time, too, for the stream widened fast. I looked up the slope again. The danger was not past, not at all, at all. No indeed. More hot steamin' lava was comin'. The flood was still increasin' and growin' wider. And a new finger of the burnin' stuff was stretchin' away from a jagged outcroppin' of rock above us. It would cut us off up ahead unless we hurried. Bejeepers, it would indeed.

" 'Come, me darlin',' I says to Balaam.

"Faith, and if I had stopped to think about it, I might of seen how strange it was for me to urge her on when herself it was that had already saved us both from the clutch of the hot stream she had just jumped.

"I pressed me knees against the mule's ribs. She quickened her pace. But it was too late. The new river of molten rock that I had seen but a few seconds before bounded down the slope, crossed our path, and spread out fast into a wide, red-flowin' flood. It grew wider and wider.

"It was too wide to jump. Much too wide, even for a mule such as Balaam.

"Begorra, I have been in many a dangerous place in and out of me military career. I have indeed. And Balaam, an agin' Army mule with a long record of campaigns, skirmishes and battles, had known war at firsthand. Armed enemy soldiers, hostile Indians, desperadoes, hazards of mountain and plain were all well-known to the both of us, but never before had man or mule faced such odds.

"There we were on a small island of hot rock between wide streams of steamin' red-hot lava. Sure, there seemed to be no escape. No escape at all, at all.

"I looked from left to right. Herself looked from right to left. Every single eye of the both of us was lookin' for some path of escape.

"Balaam's ears moved with her eyes. Those long, gray mule ears pointed for a way of escape.

"Her ears moved this way. That way. Back and forth they moved. Faster they went. Faster still. Around they went. Still faster. Now I saw her ears were movin' 'round and 'round. Those gray mule ears became misty circles of speed. Begorra, they pushed the wind down on the ground and small rocks danced away in the force of the gale.

"Those soft-haired white tips whistled through the wind as they turned. Then, bejeepers, I scarce dared to believe me own ears, for the whistle of those turnin' mule ears became a low murmur, then a rumble, a thunder, and then the sound turned into a full roar.

"And then, faith and begorra, I scarce dared to believe me own eyes, for slowly, gradually, little by little, that darlin' mule rose into the air with me sittin' on her back holdin' me breath with the surprise of it all.

"Balaam's close-roached mane fluttered as the wind from her fast-spinnin' ears struck it. Bits of rock and dirt on the trail below us blew up a cloud under the force of the ear-created draft.

"Faith, Balaam was workin' her ears as no mule ever before worked ears. She was indeed.

"Her two propeller ears beat against the air and we rose up higher, and then, fully air-borne, me and me mule sped through space, right over the boilin' stream of melted rock. Up we rose, far above the reach of the crimson cloud of steam, into the pure, fresh air of great heights.

"For the split of a minute, I can tell you, I was overcome with the excitement of the flight, and I thought of flyin' down to Colorado Springs, or to Denver, or maybe to Philadelphia or to me old home town of New York.

"But then I gave it another think. Sure, if I had flown anywhere the sight of the two of us flying along would have given people such an excitement they no doubt would have died, many of them, from the sight of it.

"And then, the telegraph wire needed repair. I must do me duty.

"Balaam reduced the speed of her propeller ears and changed their pitch. She headed for a safe spot a mile down the side of the Peak, well out of reach of the burnin' stream, and she landed on a knoll as light as a butterfly landin' on a mountain daisy.

"Sure, and I was weak in the knees when I slipped from her back. Felt as weak as an egg that has been dropped on a rock. 'Ah, me darlin',' I says to her as I ran me tremblin' hands over the length of those glorious, long but tired ears.

" 'Twas not only weak in the knees I was, but weak in the

ears, too." Sergeant O'Keefe raised his hand and rubbed his large right ear.

"Faith, it was wigglin' me own ears all the time I had been. Just like Balaam. 'Twas helpin' her I was. Or tryin' me best to help her." He twinkled a soft grin of satisfied recollection as he raised his other hand and caressed both his ears with strong, slender fingers.

"Howsomever 'tis not within me power to tell whether I helped me flyin' mule very much. Me feeble efforts may of been of some assistance, but in truth I have me doubts whether their wigglin' helped Balaam gain very much altitude," he added modestly.

"But talk about your steam engines with all of their horse power and all! Give me one mule-powered, two-propeller flyin' machine any time!

"As we stood there on the side of that steamin' mountain, with the fiery lava well behind us, we were safe and sound after a dangerous time of it, I can tell you. Then, me darlin' mule stretched her neck out and sang her lovely song as only a real Rocky Mountain canary should sing. Hee haw, hee haw. Sure, and 'twas a song that was loud and clear and sweet.

"And the echo of it came back, bright and light, and fell on the tired ears of the both of us, whether long or short, the furry white-tipped ears of a mule or the plain big ears of a sergeant in the United States Army Signal Corps.

"Sure, and it was a sweet sound, it was. Indeed it was, bejeepers."

A Rodent
Rampage

"I suppose you are glad to be down here in Colorado Springs so you can get all the news," Judge Price remarked.

"News? What news is there that is worth the while of listenin' to down here so near the level of the sea?" Sergeant O'Keefe asked. "Never a thing happens down here. 'Tis up there," he said with a sweeping gesture toward the peak that hunched majestically under a blue sky splashed with puffs of white clouds, " 'tis up there, where the air is pure and thin, that there is news and where there is strange happenin's."

Sergeant John Timothy O'Keefe and Hobbs were down in Colorado Springs on a trip for supplies. The Sergeant had greeted his friends at the telegraph office. He had sent his messages and reports. He had visited the post office and had read his mail.

"Yes, sir, strange happenin's do come about up there," he continued. "They do indeed. 'Twas this time of day, exactly two weeks ago when one of the strangest things I ever saw came to pass on the Peak.''

"What was that?'' Judge Eliphalet Price asked.

"Yes, sir. Strange it was, and turrible. Turrible indeed how those rats came after us.''

"Rats?''

"Never in all me born days have I seen so many rats,'' the Sergeant said.

"What kind of rats?'' one of the cattlemen who had joined the gathering asked.

"Why, sure now, the sugar-eatin' rats from the mountain crevasses. They had always been livin' there happy as could be and never makin' no mind. Why faith, I hardly ever saw one of them. They just kept to themselves, eatin' the sugar-like gum that oozed out of the rocks due to the volcano. And they swam late at night in the lake, leavin' a glistenin' white wake as they frolicked there in the pure water. But then that day they came. All of a sudden. Sure, and the whole world seemed like it was ankle-deep with rats. Big and small they were. Old and young. But one thing they were not. They were not fat.''

"Not fat? Why not?''

"Because they were hungry, bejeepers. They were starvin' and ready to eat anything and everything in sight. And who was in sight? What, I ask you, was in sight?''

Sergeant John Timothy O'Keefe did not wait for an answer. He was warming to his tale. "Begorra, I was in sight. And Balaam, me darlin' mule, was in sight, too. It came to me clear that I was in for a royal old time of it. I was in for the time of me young life. All alone, with me faithful mule up there on the top of the world. Alone, with the best mule ever to be enrolled in the Signal Corps of the United States Army."

"Where was Hobbs?" the Judge asked.

"Hobbs and Kit and Sweeney had gone down to the timber line for some wood. And they can thank their lucky stars for it, too. Only Balaam was there with me. If she could talk, she could give you an alarmin' description of them rodents."

"But where did these rodents come from?" asked the Judge.

"Those were the very words I asked of meself," the Sergeant replied. " 'Where did those fearful rodent creatures come from?' says I to Balaam when I first set me eyes on them.

"Then I figured it out. They were the sugar-eatin' Pikes Peak rats. Ever since the dawn of time they had been chewin' away at the saccharine oozin' out of the rocks up there. No other rock in the world is as sweet as the sugar-oozin' rocks of Pikes Peak. Those rats had been livin' the life of Riley up there, with never a care in the world."

"For goodness sake, what happened?" demanded the Judge. "Why did the rats suddenly turn on you?"

"And well may you ask," said O'Keefe. "You remember when I was down here not so long ago I told you about the volcano that melted all the snow on the Peak?"

"Yes."

"And I whitewashed it?"

"Yes."

"Sure, and after that I thought everything would be all right. But it was not all right. It was not indeed, for the heat from the volcano melted the sugar in the rocks and it flowed away in the water from the melted snow."

The Sergeant was grave. "What with no sugar in the rocks any more, the sugar-eatin' rats were faced with starvation. The great potato famine could be no worse. The good people of Ireland came to the shores of America. But the sugar-eatin' rodents of Pikes Peak had no place to go, for sugar-oozin' rocks are rare in this world. Rare indeed.

"That is not to say that those rats can survive on nothin' but the saccharine-bearin' rocks of that strange and mysterious mountain. They can eat anything, even though they prefer rock sugar. There, before me very eyes, they ate all of the mules' feed. Hay, grain and all. They ate a quarter of beef we had hangin' there, too. And then they came for me. Begorra, but it was so."

"No!" said Judge Price, always a good audience.

"Yes," said John Timothy O'Keefe. "They came straight for me and Balaam. More rats were there than ever were present in Hamelin town in Brunswick, the famous Hanover city. We were lost, me and me darlin' mule. In me bones I knew it, for no man nor beast could ever fight off that tooth-gnashin', chompin', sugar-starved horde. Quick as the kick of a mule's hind leg I retreated to the station. A strategic retreat it was, with Balaam followin' me, kickin' out at the rats this way and that.

"Inside we went, and I locked the door. 'There,' I says. 'We will be safe from those ravenous rodents!' But, no. It was not to be. They gnawed at the door, and the noise they

made as their sharp teeth shattered the wood with their millions of small bites fell on me ear like a shrill kind of thunder. A deadly soundin' noise it was, I can tell you. A doleful sound indeed, indeed it was.

"In less time than it takes to tell they had gnawed their way through the door. Balaam braced herself to kick out at them once more. And she did, too. She held them off for quite some time.

"And me? What was I doin'? I was thinkin' all of the while. Kickin', too, as they bit the soles off me shoes and the shoelaces off, as well. Something had to be done! Instanter!

"There were some pieces of stove pipe there. Short pieces that were left from fixin' the stove pipe the day before. Never was I so glad to see a few scraps of stove pipe. I upended a piece of the pipe, and put one of me feet into it. I upended another piece of stove pipe, and put me other foot in it. And there I stood, with a leg in each piece of pipe, safe from the rats for a minute anyway, for they were havin' trouble gnawin' through the metal.

"Sure, and me next thought was for Balaam. Poor creature, while her legs were flyin' like so many steam pistons, she could never hold back the tide of rats that were tryin' to make a tasty dinner out of her. Me best friend needed me help. I upended a short piece of stove pipe, and in it Balaam shoves one of her feet. I clanked meself across the room for another piece of pipe. Balaam was right there beside me, clever four-footed creature that she is, and no sooner had I upended it than in she shoved another foot. Her near front foot it was.

"Faith, now she had both front feet protected by stove

pipe. She didn't have to dance so much to guard herself. Her aim got terrific, and those hind heels of hers beat a tattoo at those mean little teeth-chompin' rats, those sugar-hungry rats. But sweet creature that she is, Balaam was still in mortal danger of bein' nibbled to death.

"I got two more pieces of stove pipe in good position. Herself saw what I was doin'. She gave a good final kick, and then settled her two hind feet down into the two new pieces of pipe I had made ready for her.

"Indeed we must of looked like strange creatures from a distant planet, standin' there with our feet and legs covered by stove pipe. But funny lookin' or not, it saved us for a time in what looked like a losin' battle. Sure and indeed, that was clear enough to me, bejeepers.

"Never before had I done such fast or more brilliant thinkin'. I was thinkin' like electricity. There! It came to me. That's it. Electricity!

"I clattered across the room in me iron socks, clankin' like a loose tin roof in a wind storm. I picked up a big coil of wire. Then, takin' one end of the wire, I fastened it to the battery connection we use to operate the telegraph up there.

"The rats had been stopped for a minute, but they would find a way to get themselves past the pipes. Sure, and I ain't sayin' they wanted to get at me so much as at Balaam, for that darlin' mule is a sweet thing and, bein' sugar-eatin' rats, they preferred her. Maybe they would nibble through the metal. Maybe they would climb over the tops. They were workin' on it. And in me bones I knew it was just a matter of time until they would be at us again.

"The electric wire was coiled tight in me hand. I threw

it with all of me might. When I let go, the wire uncoiled itself like the woundup spring of a giant clock. And clitter-clatter, clitter-clatter it went, dancin' this way and that way and every way.

"I switched on the electricity and turned it up as high as it would go. Sure, and it was lucky it was a fresh battery.

"The wire untwisted and unrolled and sprang around the room in every which way, and as it went the electricity sparked flashes of fire wherever it hit. It sparked and sparkled like a jumpin', twistin', fast-travelin' Fourth of July sparkler made up of lightnin' bolts.

"The whole station lit itself up like the midway at the Philadelphia World's Fair, with every rat that the snappin', dancin', unwindin' coil hit bein' struck down dead. Electrocuted, they were.

"Thinks I, if it strikes us, if it strikes me and Balaam, we are dead ones. Bejeepers, it looked like the both of us were not long for this world. But the fates and the saints were with us. We stood as still as rocks. The wire uncoiled around us as it unwound itself. It flipped out the door and shook itself around, this way and that way, like a long copper snake in the agonies of death. And as it uncoiled and shook itself from side to side, it hit more rats with those sharp, hot electric shocks, and they died."

"No!" said Judge Price.

"It got every last one of them, begorra. Every last one!"

"Well, what do you know?" said Eliphalet Price. Mr. Sweeney's favorite remark seemed to be the only appropriate comment.

"I leaned over and turned the current off at the same

time the wire stopped uncurlin' and had come to rest.

"I swept what was left of the rats out of the station, and just as I was wonderin' how I could clean the yard up, along came a storm. It was a squall, I can tell you. Maybe you saw it from down here. A big, black cloud. Sure, and it was the worst storm I ever saw in all of me years on the summit, and I have seen some storms up there, you can be sure of that. It rained like I never saw it rain before. Or since, for that matter.

"Me and Balaam was still in the station, wonderin' if it would stand up under the flood or if the building would be washed away. Finally it stopped rainin' and I stepped out the door, with me faithful mule at me side, and there was not a rat in sight. The cloudburst had washed them all away, and the whole Peak was as bare as if they had never been there at all, at all."

The Sergeant was solemn in the silence that followed. "Faith, and it may be that all of this may sound a wee bit strange to a person who wasn't there at the time. But I can prove every single word I say is the solemn truth."

No question was raised. No question but that contained in the silence. John Timothy O'Keefe looked up from his seat on the bench.

"Hobbs," he said, "that day you went down to the timber line for wood. Wasn't that two weeks ago today?"

"Yes," Hobbs answered. Hobbs was a soldier with a solemn, truthful face. "Yes. Two weeks ago today, Johnny."

"And did you see it rainin' up on the summit when you were down there at the timber line?"

"Sure did. Looked like it might of rained a lot up there.

It was a real black cloud."

"And wasn't it just about this time of the day?" Sergeant O'Keefe insisted.

"Yes, Johnny. Just about this time of day," Hobbs agreed.

"And when you got back to the station, do you remember me tellin' you what had happened when you were gone?"

"Yes, I sure do, Johnny," Hobbs admitted.

"And did I tell you just exactly what I just now told about the rats?" asked the Sergeant calmly but firmly.

"Yes. That you did, Johnny. The same thing. Exactly the same," Hobbs replied.

"Now, tell me this, Hobbs. Have you seen any sugar-eatin' rats since then?"

"Since then? No, I ain't, Johnny," said Hobbs.

"There!" said O'Keefe triumphantly. "You see? And look there." He pointed to his shoes. "I had to have me shoes half-soled, and I got new shoelaces, too. I guess that proves it, hey?"

After a pause, he added, "I don't think there is a single Pikes Peak sugar-eatin' rat left up there. Gone! Gone with the wild pigeon, the great auk and the dodo bird! Sure, and I doubt, too, that the sugar rocks will ever be as sweet as they used to be!"

"Well, what do you know?" muttered Judge Price.

Balaam Goes
AWOL

"I HAVE SEEN a great many strange things in me day, that I have indeed." Sergeant John Timothy O'Keefe spoke with conviction.

He looked at the mules with an affectionate eye. His gaze took in the burros standing near them and came back to rest on the beauties of Balaam. The drowsy slit of her eyes, the slope of her ears, slant of her rump and shudder of her shoulder were pure beauty to the Sergeant.

"Sure, strange things have I seen," the soldier continued, as his eyes turned toward the massive hulk of stone that loomed above them on the horizon. Now he gazed at the distant, dizzy heights of Pikes Peak.

" 'Tis up there where they happen. Up there in the pure, thin air of the majestic heights where it's been decreed that I must carry on me labors.

"In the common, lower parts of the world, common things happen. In the rarified air of the Peak, rare things occur. Rare indeed."

57

Judge Eliphalet Price and Mr. Sweeney listened to the comments of O'Keefe in respectful silence.

"It all happened because the Army Signal Corps in its, pardon the word, wisdom decided to reduce the mules' rations. I warned them not to do it. Sure, and I know mules, indeed I do, and I told them a mule is a soldier, and a soldier needs rations aplenty. But 'No,' they said. 'Cut the mules' rations,' they said.

"I had to account for the hay and the grain. Forms and red tape aplenty, you may be sure, even if there was not to be rations aplenty. Since I couldn't feed her regular mule's feed, I fed me darlin' hominy, dried apples and biscuits out of the soldiers' mess. But I couldn't keep that up. Not forever.

"So, bein' a soldier meself, and bound to follow orders, I done me duty, even though it broke me heart to do so, indeed it did. The mules understood it was none of me own doin', but they didn't like it. Not a bit. Balaam's face got as long as four stormy days in a row.

"Sure, Balaam is a mule that is different. Wise she is, and independent. And while every good Army mule always plays the loyal part of a faithful soldier, mules do not solemnly swear to uphold the constitution of the United States. Neither do they swear faithfully to obey the orders of all duly constituted superior officers.

"Mules, however, being sensible creatures, do in fact uphold the constitution of the United States without any kicks or brayin' to the contrary. In all of me born days, never have I seen an Army mule fail to uphold the constitution.

"But!" The word exploded from the Sergeant's mouth

and the carefully trimmed hairs on his upper lip stuck straight out for a moment. "Obeyin' the commands of superior officers is something else again!"

"A horse of a different color?" asked Judge Price helpfully.

"Indeed it is," the Sergeant agreed. "At the very least, a mule of a different color. Everybody knows it takes a good ration of oats to keep a mule's soul stuck to her body. And a hay-burner has got to have hay to burn.

"Balaam, she didn't take to bein' on short rations. She didn't like it. Not at all, at all. I kept her tight hobbled. I used two halters on her. I locked her in the barn. Oh, I can tell you, her brayin' was something sad to hear. She complained in loud and mournful tones. The joyous singing of a Rocky Mountain canary became the doleful, heart-breakin' brays of a mule in the anguish of reduced rations and impending starvation.

"Her baleful brays went out into space from the mountain's top. They echoed around in the canyons and bounced back from the other mountains. The world was filled with her sorrowful song.

"One of the most solemn of her brays struck the Spanish Peaks, two hundred miles to the south. Powerful that bray was. Powerful indeed, but so great was the distance, the echo didn't arrive back at the Peak from whence it started for two-and-a-half days.

"Mules, like soldiers, need plenty of rations. So in her anguish Balaam made up her mind she was not goin' to be abused by any such thing as reduced rations. Sure, and a soldier wouldn't do it, but faith and begorra, she did. Sure, a mule she is and she was workin' like a mule and they started supplying rations for a canary, but not a Rocky Mountain canary. All in all, they were treatin' her like a dog. Yes, they wanted to work her like a mule, feed her like a bird, and treat her like a dog. She deserted."

"Deserted?" Sweeney asked. "I've never heard about Balaam deserting. This must have been before I was assigned to the Peak."

"Well, maybe not deserted," replied O'Keefe. "She was not sworn to obey the foolish commands of commandin' officers. Maybe she just went absent without leave. But she was gone."

"No!" said Sweeney.

O'Keefe pondered over the thought for a moment. "Gone! Vanished! Vamoosed!"

"Well, what do ye know?" said Sweeney.

"Locked doors mean nothin' to Balaam. That dapple-gray mule is not only intelligent, she is a genius, I can tell you. You might just as well not lock a door to keep her under control. If she wants anything, she'll get it."

Balaam, standing at the hitching rail with Kit, flapped her long gray ears, turned her head, and blinked her eyes in appreciation of the tribute.

There was no doubt about it. Balaam was trim, battle-scarred and beautiful. She was strong and capable. Wisdom sparkled in those big, lustrous mule eyes. Even the tilt of her ears spoke of knowledge.

Sergeant John Timothy O'Keefe continued. "Knowin' mules as I do, and knowin' Balaam in particular, I knew what had happened. But a soldier's life is a soldier's life. I would have to do me best to find her and return her to the unfortunate existence of inadequate rations. But sure, thinks I, bein' AWOL like that might bring the matter to the attention of the commandin' general and the rations might be increased.

"That mule was puttin' up a fight for every mule in the Signal Corps. It was her way of sayin' that more rations were needed. I reported the information of her absence and the cause of it, hopin' all the while that the orders would be countermanded.

"Then the telegraph wire broke. Hobbs and Kit couldn't find the break. Sure, and 'twas up to me. But what could I do without me faithful mule? Sure, and 'tis herself who is the best at findin' the breaks in the wires. Seems to smell them out, she does. Like a rabbit dog can smell out rabbits, that elegant mule can smell out the breaks in the wires. Leastways, it seems she does.

"Well, the name and reputation of the United States Army Signal Corps was hangin' in the balance, it was indeed. That broken wire had to be found, and it had to be fixed. Balaam was needed. She was needed bad, indeed she was. So I went out to look for her.

"I had a notion where she was, for I had observed a band of wild horses from the Peak. They were in the valley to the south. I soon found them, and there she was, livin' the life of Riley, runnin' around with the wild horses.

"There was no reduction of rations there. Balaam and those horses were knee-deep in bunch grass and wild clover.

"Now in me day I have seen many a wild horse, but never a one like these. Black they were, and they had white tails

and manes. Pure white, and the longest I had ever seen. Begorra, they were so long they dragged on the ground. Every single one of them. And do you know what?"

"No. What?" Sweeney asked obligingly.

"Faith, and Balaam had grown a long tail, too. It was draggn' down on the ground, just like those wild horses' tails."

"No!" said Sweeney.

"And her mane had grown, too. Clear down to the ground, just like the horses. Herself was tryin' to look like those wild horses. Her dapples were gettin' darker, too. Fact is, they were almost black. And all this happened in only two days' time, bejeepers. But then, Balaam is a remarkable mule.

"Well, I couldn't get within 860 yards of that mule. But some mountain lions did. I could see it all as clear as day, for I was standin' on a small knoll overlooking the valley. Fierce those mountain lions were, and hungry. They sprang with no delay on the nearest horse, and down he went in the clutches of their claws.

"Sure, and I thought that beautiful horse, with his sleek, black hide and his long, white mane and tail that dragged on the ground, was not long for this world.

"But it was not to be. Far from it. Balaam jumped and hit the ground runnin'. She came on the run, as fast as I ever saw a mule go, with her long tail and mane flyin' in the wind and streamin' out behind her like an ocean wave breakin' up against a length of sandy beach. And her hair was standin' on end. Bejeepers, I never saw that in a mule, either before or since. A cat, maybe, but never did I see it in a mule. Never at all, at all. It was somethin' to behold, sure and it was, indeed it was.

" 'Hee haw,' she went, and it sounded as fierce as the battle cry of a Sioux warrior.

" 'Hee haw, hee haw,' she went again, like a bugle commandin' a brigade to charge."

"No," said Sweeney.

"Like a bugle," O'Keefe insisted.

"What do ye know!" Sweeney exclaimed.

"Balaam arrived at the scene of battle as quick as greased lightnin'. She wheeled left, put herself into reverse, lifted her hind legs, and fired! Her heels shot out like two batterin' rams, and they hit the first lion in the brisket and away he went, flying through the air, rump over appetite.

" 'Hee haw,' she went and, bang! More heels shot out again and the second lion followed suit and spun through the air like the darin' young man on the flyin' trapeze.

"He hit the dirt with a thud and resumed the attack. Approaching with teeth bared and claws extended, he looked for all the world like a buzz saw, and he was screamin' like one likewise.

"But that mule didn't kick again," O'Keefe said slowly.

"What happened?" asked Sweeney.

"Yes, whatever happened?" asked Judge Price.

"When the lion came close—"

"Yes?"

"That fine broth of a mule—"

"Yes?"

"She just opened her mouth—"

"Yes?"

"Sure, and she bit that lion's head right off!"

"No!" said Sweeney.

"Indeed she did, and then she bit the head right off the other lion who was comin' at her in a most unfriendly manner."

"Well, what do ye know?" said Sweeney.

"And the wild horses, with their long tails and their manes flyin', whinneyed their thanks to Balaam and off they ran, up a canyon deep into the heart of the Sangre de Cristo mountains.

"I can tell you, I was that surprised, I was indeed," the Sergeant added.

"I am considerably surprised myself," Judge Price commented.

"Balaam didn't follow them. She had saved them from the lions and I guess she decided to come back to soldierin', reduced rations or not. She had had her fling.

"She spotted me on the ridge and she could see that I needed her. Seemed to know the United States Army Signal Corps was in distress tryin' to get along without her. She came right along with me. Duty called her and she responded.

"Sure, and she searched out that broken wire in jig time. Hobbs and Kit couldn't find the break. I never could have found it alone. But she did. She found it right away.

"I spliced the wire and once again the weather reports went buzzin' over the wires to the waitin' world. The news of Balaam's heroic rescue of the wild horses from the mountain lions reached the ears of the commandin' general. Also he learned the reason for her goin' AWOL. He ordered full rations again, although I heard that it was his wife that made him do it. Sure, mules and soldiers need full rations.

"I trimmed Balaam's tail down to regulation length, and I roached her mane. And I know that is a bit of a tale, and there may be those of a suspicious nature that may doubt what I say. But I can prove it. Every word. It's the solemn truth."

"How can you prove it?" asked Judge Price.

"Even though Balaam grew that long tail and mane in two days when she was with the wild horses, they haven't grown that fast since then. Look. You can see for yourself. And if you want to come up to the weather station I'll show you the very clippers I used to do the trimmin' with."

Sergeant O'Keefe pointed to his faithful friend with pride. "Sure, and like I say, I was that surprised. I was indeed," said John Timothy O'Keefe.

The Sergeant
Shoots a Deer

"IT HAS BEEN a good long time, it has, since I was down to Colorado Springs, but it will be a longer time, I hope, before I forget what befell me and me faithful mule Balaam in the early winter of last year. It happened on the last trip back to the Peak before we became snowbound."

Sergeant John Timothy O'Keefe was speaking. It was early spring, and in the telegraph office the fire burned brightly in the big potbellied stove. Its warmth was welcome, for there was still a considerable chill in the air.

"What was that, Sergeant?" asked Judge Eliphalet Price.

"I was on me way back to the Peak, I was. The trail wound over the foothills and between the giant boulders and rock formations.

"I was astride Balaam and that darlin' stepped light and sure on the rocky trail. Pink sparks shot away from the click of her small iron shoes on the rock. Sharp blue sparks danced now and then away from the mule's shoes as they struck against the icy earth."

68

"Sparks came from the earth?" asked the Judge.

"It was a cold day," Sergeant O'Keefe replied, "and the ground was frozen hard. Never before had I see the earth frozen so flint hard that it threw off sparks at the touch of iron. Sure, and I wished I had me instruments there, for I would like to know the depth of the temperature that made the earth so hard.

"Kit, the bay mule, with Hobbs astride followed close after me and Balaam.

"The trail slipped around a jagged tower of rough boulders. More than a dozen miles remained of the seventeen miles we had to go to reach the top. Snow began to fall gently from a lead-gray sky. Sure, and it was a silent world and it seemed to hold a prophecy of strange events to come. And it is strange events they were indeed, I am sure you will agree when you hear them.

"I pulled Balaam to a stop. Hobbs drew up alongside of the two of us. 'It's a cold day, Sergeant,' he says.

"I didn't answer. Instead, I pointed ahead. We were facin' a rough chain of trees that crowned the point of a small, steep ridge and fell with the ridge down to a sheltered valley. There both the trees and the ridge ended.

"Through the dust of snow I saw a deer pokin' his noggin out from behind the wall of trees. The close, thick trunks hid the rest of the deer. Sure, and a fine deer it was, though his small head, with bright eyes, quiverin' nostrils and restless ears, was all I could see.

"A long distance away it was, but I couldn't help thinkin' how tasty a haunch of venison would be for dinner when we got back to the station. I was armed with a revolver. A .32

caliber Smith and Wesson it was. Not a proper weapon for a deer. Much too small it was, and I was not sure how accurate it would be at that distance. Nonetheless, I figured I might be able to put a bullet in the eye and bring the creature down.

"I signaled me intention to Hobbs. Balaam seemed to know what I was about and moved forward as silent as a dapple-gray ghost.

"I narrowed the distance as much as I thought I could without scarin' the deer away. Sure, and I knew the deer had not seen us or he would have run away. He held his pose, sniffin' the air. If he felt something was wrong, he didn't show it.

"The distance was still too far for that small weapon, but I figured I had to chance a shot. If I waited longer, I thought, the deer would be sure to see me and run.

"I raised me revolver, and I took careful aim, and I fired.

"The creature's head disappeared. 'Missed,' I said. 'He's gone for good now.'

"Hobbs came alongside again and stopped. 'Never mind,' he says. 'A long shot it was. Too long. I didn't see how you could hit him anyway.'

" 'Wait,' said I. 'Look! There he is again!'

"Faith, and 'twas true. That cautious head poked itself out from behind the trees once more. First time a deer ever gave me a second shot in the same place.

"I raised me revolver again. Real careful aim I took this time, you may be sure.

"Bang, went the gun, but the report sounded small, absorbed by the white blanket of snow that covered the ground and lay heavy on the trees and by the soft grayness in the air.

"The deer's head drew back behind the trees to safety. 'Missed again, bejeepers,' said I.

" 'Too bad,' said Hobbs. 'Maybe you could have gotten him if you'd been closer.'

" 'Could be,' said I, but I was gettin' just a little bit riled. Then I looked up. 'It's a bit of a wonder,' I remarked as calm as I could, 'but there he is again!'

" 'Can't be,' says Hobbs.

" ' 'Tis,' says I.

" 'That deer must have a hard streak of curiosity,' Hobbs whispered.

" 'Curiosity, they say, killed a cat.' I turned to Hobbs. 'It is now me fondest wish that curiosity and this Smith and Wesson in me hand may kill that deer. Me aim, I am hopin', is better this time.'

"I raised me gun and fired. The creature's head drew back again.

" 'Bad luck,' Hobbs murmurs to me.

"Sure, never again did I think I would have three chances given to me to kill a creature as skittish as a deer. And, begorra, do you know that that deer poked his noggin out from behind those trees again!

"Once again I raised me small weapon. Once again it spoke and faith, once again the deer's head disappeared behind the trees and there was no deer there at all, at all.

" 'The snow is what does it,' remarked Hobbs.

" 'No, 'tis not the snow,' I insisted. ' 'Tis no more and no less than that I was once a better shot than I am now.'

" 'It's the weapon, then,' said Hobbs. 'It's too small.'

" 'True it is, the gun is small,' I admitted, 'but 'tis a good weapon and if I hit him in the right place he should drop.'

"And then me eyes narrowed and I drew back in disbelief, for there the deer was yet again. There he was with his cautious head and bright eyes and pointin' ears. I fired again, and the deer pulled his head back again.

" 'Give me one more shot and if I miss, sure I will very seriously consider being on me way with no deer at all, at all, for me pains,' said I.

" 'Then, shoot, for there he is again,' remarked Hobbs.

"I had adjusted for the wind and the distance and the snow, so I shot again. Once more the deer drew back his head.

"Oh, I was that dismayed. It went on and on. I fired. The deer pulled back, and then stuck his noggin out again.

"Sure, I shot all me cartridges. Seventeen in all. And I had me mouth all fixed for venison to while away that cold winter evenin' with.

"All them shots and me with no deer at all, at all. 'Tis sore distressed I was, I can tell you. 'Twas a day as cold as a polar bear's nose in January. I dismounted and loosened me saddle girth. Balaam took a deep breath. When she blew, part of her white, steamin' cloud of breath caught in the freezin' cold, turned into small crystals, and tinkled soft as they fell and shattered against the frozen trail.

"Suddenly Hobbs nudged me. 'Look!'

"I raised me head and never before have I ever seen so many deer. The line of animals extended from behind the trees to a rock-hidden mouth of a canyon on the opposite side of the valley and they were movin' at a brisk trot.

" 'Ah well, let them pass,' said I. 'They deserve to go un-molested in view of me poor marksmanship.'

"We watched them pass. One hour and thirty-seven minutes it took them to go by. I had never seen so many deer in one herd.

"We mounted our mules and went on. The trail led to the place where the deer had stuck his noggin out from behind the trees so many times.

"When we got there, Balaam stopped short. She lifted her head and brayed loud and long. 'Hee haw,' she went, like she does when she is happy.

"I looked down. 'Bejeepers, look at that!' I could hardly believe my own eyes.

"Hobbs caught up with me. 'Well, I'll be jiggered,' was all he could say.

"I lifted me finger and counted. 'One, two, three, four.' Me finger continued to rise and fall. 'Fifteen, sixteen, seventeen,' I finished."

"But what had you found?" interrupted Judge Price. "What were you counting?"

"Seventeen deer."

"No!" said Eliphalet Price.

"They were layin' right there in a little gully behind the trees. Me aim had been good and I had killed a deer with each shot. He fell down out of sight, and another came along and stuck his noggin out, and I shot him, too. Shot each one of them right in the eye, just where I had aimed.

"Hobbs was tremblin' like an aspen leaf in a storm. Sure, and the revolver didn't make much noise, bein' so small and with the snow and all. When I had shot all of me seventeen cartridges the rest of the herd continued walking across the valley and into the canyon.

"Faith, I didn't want seventeen deer, but we could use them before the winter was over. We put all of our gear and supplies on Kit, and then Hobbs rode on ahead. I lashed the deer tails together and threw them over Balaam in front of the saddle. It was piled so high they were that I could hardly see over them when I was mounted. But I had no use to see, for Balaam knew the trail."

Judge Price looked quizzically at the Sergeant.

" 'Tis sorry I am that Hobbs has been transferred to the Mexican border, for no doubt he could add some interestin' details that I have overlooked. Yes, sir, too bad it is that Hobbs is not here to tell you about that time with the deer," said Sergeant O'Keefe.

A Fight to
the Finish

O N HIS LAST trip up Pikes Peak before being snowbound for the winter at the weather station at its top, Sergeant John Timothy O'Keefe had shot seventeen deer with seventeen shots. And with a revolver at that. It was a feat that some might find difficult to believe, but he had told of it with his usual becoming modesty. His frank open face and his obvious candor washed away the stains of doubt.

"I was that surprised meself," he said. "But that was nothin' at all compared to what happened after that. Nothin' at all, at all."

That day had been a winter's day, and winter up there near the top of the Peak, at the gate of heaven, is like winter nowhere else, Sergeant O'Keefe maintained. "Sure, and the Signal Corps couldn't have picked a better spot for a weather station, begorra," he remarked. "There's an awful lot of weather up there.

"It was cold that day," he continued, "and it had been

snowin'. Hobbs had gone on ahead with Kit and the supplies. The snow came down faster and the wind increased. By the time I had lashed those seventeen deer across Balaam's back, Hobbs was lost to sight. For a while the snow was as thick as feathers in a pillow fight when a pillow busts. I could see it would be hard travel, but I thought Balaam could make the remainin' distance to the station in spite of the storm. A bit of unusual weather could prevent our reachin' the top, but me fondest hope was that we could make it.

"But it was not the weather we had to worry about, begorra, though on the wind it was that the first news of danger reached me ears. I heard a sound in the distance. Shrill and severe it was. At first I thought it was the wind blowin' through the ice-covered trees. But, no. That was not it. Not at all, at all. It was the shrill, coarse wail of mountain lions. When I heard their distant cries, sure I knew it was the rage of hunger that drove them out to hunt in such a bitter storm.

"The sounds sent a chill through me already cold frame. And through Balaam's, too. Faith, and neither of us had much longin' to be turned into dinner for a pack of mountain lions.

"Danger is not new to me, and as I pushed me way through that blizzard I breathed a fervent wish that the lions would not find our trail in the storm. Me and me darlin' mule and seventeen fresh killed deer would make a tasty dish for those ferocious beasts. Sure, and I did not fail to realize that I was unarmed. Me seventeen cartridges had been spent on seventeen black-tailed deer and me Smith and Wesson was useless as a fly swatter.

"The shrill cries of the lions seemed to get lower in pitch and increase in intensity, and I knew they must of found the place where the deer had been shot. There was a chance, not a big one, but a chance, they would follow the trail in the wrong direction. Or they might follow the herd of deer that had passed that way. But most likely they would follow me and me heavily laden mule. Begorra, the trail of the fresh carcasses we carried would be hard for even one hungry mountain lion to miss.

"Balaam was bravely puttin' the distance behind her. We were well out of the foothills, and the sturdy creature was laborin' with a steep trail.

"Then the sounds that came to me on the wind changed, they did, they did indeed. The beasts were on to the trail for sure, and it took only a minute for me to tell which trail they had picked up. It was our trail, and the cries carried to me on the freezin' wind were gettin' louder.

"I glanced back. The beasts were visible through the swirlin' snow. Bad it looked. Indeed it did. But then a thought came to me, and I knew what I was going to do. If I waited much longer it would be too late. When another leap would bring them close enough to tear me out of the saddle, I threw one of the deer over me shoulder.

"It was a right thought. The lions sprang for the carcass and, in a snarlin' scramble, fought each other for its possession. No one of them won the prize. All of them shared in the fight and in nothin' flat the deer was gone. Sure, and I noticed that one of them got injured in that battle, but me and Balaam had more pressin' matters to attend to. We continued our climb up the trail, thankful for a bit of time in which to do it.

"It didn't take the lions long to catch up again. And when they did, I dropped another deer. They stopped again to fight for it, and we made some more distance.

"Once again they roared up the trail after us. And once again when they came close and I felt I was not long for this world I tossed another deer to them.

"Again they stopped to gobble up the deer, and when I glanced back that time, begorra, 'twas a fierce scene that met me eyes, indeed it was. The creatures were all atop each other, makin' uncommon ferocious sounds. But there was no time to spend gazin' at such a fierce sight.

" 'If the deer hold out, we may make it to the station,' I whispered to me faithful mule. Every time we dropped a deer, Balaam's load got lighter and the lions' load got heavier. It was a slight hope, and in me heart I knew it. The snow was heavier now and it was deeper under foot. Balaam was slowin' down even though the load was made lighter every time I dropped a deer. But I thought maybe the lions would eat so much deer they would stop chasin' us.

"But you never saw such hungry mountain lions! Bejeepers, they made short work of each deer. Finally, I threw the ninth one to the ground, and this time as I looked back, sure, and they not only ate up the deer but gobbled up the lion at the bottom of that pile of snarlin' beasts, too.

"Me one thought was that it was a good thing, for now there was one less lion. The best of all Army mules meanwhile continued to climb. Each time the lions caught up I would toss off another deer, and Balaam made some distance on them. Each time another lion would get eaten up. Must of been the weakest ones, or maybe they just made mistakes and didn't stop to find out where a deer left off and the nearest mountain lion began.

"Then, begorra, I saw that me calculations were all wrong. The fresh red meat they were getting was makin' them stronger. They weren't getting satisfied at all, at all. The deer were disappearing and so were the mountain lions, but the remainin' beasts were in better shape than ever.

"Off went the fourteenth deer. The cougars tackled it and tackled each other. Off went the fifteenth deer, and the battle for it was just as fierce. Off went the sixteenth, and it took no great amount of figurin' to figure that there was just one deer left. Sure, and the fact that there were only two lions left did not escape me. But, begorra, two strong, well-fed but still hungry, ferocious mountain lions chasin' you is not a warmin' thought in the middle of a Pikes Peak blizzard.

"I would have to face the two of them hand to hand, or more likely hand to claw, you might say. But perhaps Balaam could be saved. I tossed off the seventeenth deer, then dismounted and slapped me mule on the rump. Sure, 'twas like a partin' handclasp with an old friend. She didn't want to leave me. Like a command it was, though, and like the good soldier that she is, she obeyed and walked off into the storm up the trail toward the station.

"I turned to face the two remainin' beasts. Me heart was in me throat, and me knife was in me hand. They had just finished off that last deer and I was expectin' the worst. And

then I saw something the like of which I never hope to see again. Instead of comin' after me, begorra, those two fierce creatures turned to face each other.

"I hoped that maybe they were no longer hungry. A fond hope it was, but a hopeless hope. They paused for a minute that seemed long enough to stretch from here to Cheyenne Mountain. Then, one of them licked a chop. The other lion looked at him and, not to be outdone, licked a chop of his own. The first one licked his other chop. So did the other one. Then they both licked their chops, me lookin' on all the while, not knowin' what might happen, and havin' no good place to turn.

"They licked their chops again. Then they looked at me. It was a delicate situation, to be sure. I was hopin' all the while they would not mistake me for a chop. Then they looked at each other and one of the beasts growled a small but ferocious growl. The other snarled a vicious snarl. The growler growled once more, and the snarler snarled again.

"Me ears bent forward and me eyes bugged out an inch-and-a-half and the knuckles on the hand that held the knife were white. The growler was not to be outdone, and there was nothin' else to do, so he took a bite out of the snarler. A small kind of bite. The snarler exploded into a paroxysm of rage, and bit him back. But he took a bigger bite. Those lions were angry, I can tell you, indeed they were. They bit again, each bite bigger than the last one. They snarled and they roared and, in a flash, they were locked in a battle to the finish.

"And finish it was, for, bejeepers, before me very eyes, on

the frozen snow-covered trail to Pikes Peak, those two mountain lions ate each other up!

"When I saw it, I was that surprised," said John Timothy O'Keefe. "I was indeed."

Mr. Sweeney, when he heard the story, was surprised, too. "Well, what do ye know?" he said.

The Night the
Wind Blew

"SURE, AND there is more weather on the top of Pikes Peak than anywhere else, whether you believe it or not," said Sergeant John Timothy O'Keefe.

Judge Eliphalet Price sat up straight and smoothed the wrinkles out of his vest. The yellow line of his gold watch chain looped evenly down from the bottom pocket and up sharply through the top buttonhole, from whence it dropped down on the other side of his long, thin, tight-fitting garment until it turned up again to dart into the other pocket.

"The fearful cold and the bitter freezin' winds are always snappin' the wires or blowin' tree limbs down on them. And a busted telegraph wire is a hushed and silent telegraph wire, which is no wire at all, at all," continued O'Keefe.

"A soldier and a mule in the service of the United States Army Signal Corps on top of that towerin' high mountain live a turrible hard life. Turrible hard indeed.

"On this day that is in me mind, suddenly the wires went

dead. Nothin' was on them at all, at all. Nothin' but a long and thunderin' silence. Sure, and 'twas up to me, bein' sergeant and all, and me dapple-gray darlin' to fix it.''

Sergeant O'Keefe gazed fondly out the window at Balaam tied to the hitching rail. That greatest of all Army mules, one of the most valuable creatures in all the world, was standing quietly. Many an adventure had been shared by the two, and the look in her eye matched the look in the eye of John Timothy O'Keefe.

"It had been snowin' for a week," continued the Sergeant. "The drifts were deep. We plowed along through them, me and herself, that dapple-gray sweetheart that can smell out the breaks in the wires.

"She found the break, as I knew she would, and I fixed it. It was the bitter cold that had snapped the wire. Then we turned toward the top, thinkin' of the warm fire and the warm friends and food that would be waitin' for us at the signal station. Little did we know of the turrible hard time that was in store for us.

"Lookin' off into the winterswept space of the land far below the mountain I saw the line of a blizzard sweepin' toward us. I could see it comin' plain. Across the ridge of the jagged peaks that stretched away from us it came. Indeed it did. Came like the roarin', snow-filled, icebound cyclone that it was.

"Then it hit us hard, herself and me, there on the left side of the top of the world. It was as cold as an iceberg's heart, and the snow came down on us like a thousand white bed sheets flappin' in the frigid wind.

"It was hard goin'. I recognized no landmarks after a

minute's time, but Balaam made her sure-footed way. I was ready to admit that I was lost and I hoped—no, indeed I knew—the mule, dear creature, would know the proper direction. Sure, on a trail that wound up the sides of canyons, a mistake in even one step could bring us both to destruction.

"It was gettin' dark and I knew we would have to stop for the night. But I thought we could make ourselves comfortable in spite of the storm.

"I saw a small tree juttin' out of the snow-filled world. It was only a few feet away. I turned me mule toward it. Faith, and she didn't want to go.

" 'Get over there,' I said, 'so I can tie you to the tree and keep you from wanderin' away before the icy wind.'

"Still she resisted. I thought that was strange for, while Balaam is a mule and she can be stubborn as a mule sometimes is, she is not balky.

"Finally, and over the most serious protests of herself, and with much pushin' and pullin' and the use of me most persuasive mule driver's language, I got her tied to the small tree. I carefully arranged her blanket over her to protect her from the bitter cold and the snow.

"Sure, and we were lost for sure. There were no other trees around. Only this little one, and there should have been many big trees if we were on the trail. Thinks I, maybe even me mule has got herself lost in this fierce storm.

"I strapped her blanket tight to her so it wouldn't slip off. When I had taken care of Balaam, I began to prepare me own quarters for the night. Just then the wind changed direction and Balaam turned around so that her rump would face the wind.

"Sure, the wind might change again, thought I. So I moved a bit away from the mule so she wouldn't step on me if she decided to change her direction again, too.

" 'Twas a turrible cold night. I was gettin' so cold I was blue as a pigeon. Turrible cold, and there was no good shelter to be had. But a few feet away from where Balaam might circle around, into me own blankets I crawled. And cold as it was, I was that snug and warm on the inside, and soon I was fast asleep.

"I don't know how long I slept, but when I woke up I could tell that the wind had died down because there was no movement of wind around me like there was when I went to sleep.

"I let meself out of me bed, and when I looked about, faith, I was in a strange place. The night before I had gone to sleep in a barren place, but I woke up in a forest. Instead of the bare, snow-covered place and only one little twig of a tree, sure, there were tall trees all about.

"Begorra, as you might know, I couldn't imagine what had happened. There was a sheer rock wall on one side and near it a giant of a tree, with lots of other trees, smaller ones, all around. Me first thought was of me mule, but the darlin' creature was nowhere about. What had happened to her? Where could she have gone? Where did the trees come from?

"I thought I could hear her brayin', singing a sad, faraway song. But I couldn't tell where she was.

"Then, of a sudden, not knowin' quite why, I looked up. And there at the top of the largest tree, up in the sky, I saw me mule. She was hangin' by her halter and she was tied to

the top of the tallest tree. The tree that shot up near the cliff. And then I knew what had happened. The canyon was all drifted full of snow the night before when we went to sleep. That little tree I saw was only the top of the tallest tree in the canyon. All the others were covered with snow.

"The wind had changed in the middle of the night and had blown all the snow out of the canyon. I had been sleepin' on the snow and as it blew away I had been lowered gently to the bottom. But poor Balaam, she was tied to the top of the tallest tree. When the snow blew away it left her tied up there. And there she was, danglin' from the top of a tree, up there near where the trail alongside the canyon wall was. Tied like a shiny star to the tip of a Christmas tree, she was.

" 'Twas me own fault. Balaam had been on the trail the night before. Sure, it was a trail invisible to everyone except that sweet Rocky Mountain canary. Little wonder it was that she had objected to bein' tied up to the top of that tree. She knew it was off the trail.

"Sure, if I had only thought. If I had only realized that trail-wise creature knew that tree was off the trail. And there she was, tied to the top of it, danglin' up there near heaven, and there was I, with no way to get her down."

"Well, what did you do?" Judge Price interrupted. "A mule way up at the top of a tree is in truth a bit of a predicament."

"Sure, and before I could even so much as think about how to get her down, a new blast of wind hit me," replied Sergeant O'Keefe. "Such a wind as I have never seen before it was. The world was filled with the whirlin', swirlin' snow again. There was nothin' I could do in such a wind to rescue me darlin' mule. To save me own skin I crawled back into me blankets again. The wind kept up somethin' fierce. I could tell from the way I was tossed around, though I was safe and snug inside me sugans.

"Faith, I had no way of knowin' what was happenin' except I was sure it was the worst windy storm in a coon's age. As long as me mule was in such dire circumstances I had no wish to live meself. The wind blew and blew and I was tossed around in me blankets for a long time.

"Finally the wind died down and everything was still again. Cautious-like I pushed me nose out of me bed. By this time I was prepared for anything. That is, I was prepared for anything except what really happened. I was in a place where there were no trees. Only snow all around me. There was only one tree. A small tree, and Balaam was tied to it!

"I could scarce believe me eyes. I wondered if it was a ghost, a dapple-white ghost of an Army mule that had come to a strange end. I got up and walked to it. I put out me hand to touch it. It was no ghost! It was me own darlin' Balaam. She lifted up her head and she sang, hee haw, hee haw! Faith, I never before heard such beautiful music. No ghost could make such beautiful music as that Rocky Mountain canary. An angel, perhaps, but a ghost, never!

"Then it came to me what had happened. The wind had changed a second time, and had blown all the snow back into the canyon, and I had been lifted up on the snow as the canyon was filled up again."

"No!" said Judge Eliphalet Price.

"It stands to reason that if the wind blew the snow out of the canyon, it could blow the snow back in and fill it up again."

"Well what do you know!" the Judge exclaimed.

"I untied Balaam and let her follow the trail to the summit. Never again will I fail to understand the wisdom of that Rocky Mountain canary. Never again will I ever doubt the intelligence of that darlin' of an Army mule," said Sergeant John Timothy O'Keefe.

THE AUTHOR

HAROLD W. FELTON, a lawyer by profession, has long been interested in American folklore. The first of his widely acclaimed books was an anthology of legends about Paul Bunyan, and since that time he has pursued folk heroes and tall tales with enthusiasm. His stories about Pecos Bill, John Henry, Fire-Fightin' Mose, Bowleg Bill, Ed Grant and the rest rank him as a master yarnspinner. His keen sense of humor and his determined pursual of available facts and authentic source material are again reflected in his presentation of Sergeant O'Keefe's adventures.

Born in the Midwest, this popular author now lives in Jackson Heights, New York, where he devotes his leisure time to writing for young people.

THE ARTIST

LEONARD EVERETT FISHER, whose striking scratchboard drawings bring to life the humorous Sergeant O'Keefe, is a versatile artist whose outstanding illustrations have enhanced numerous books for young readers. He holds a Master of Fine Arts degree from Yale University, and has been the recipient of art prizes and fellowships, including the Pulitzer Art Prize and awards by the American Institute of Graphic Arts. His work has been exhibited in galleries and touring exhibits.

Recently Mr. Fisher has illustrated and designed his own picture books in addition to his other creative work in the juvenile book field. His studio is in Westport, Connecticut, where he lives with his family.